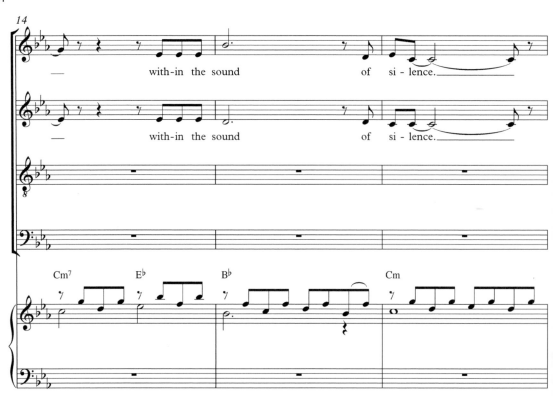

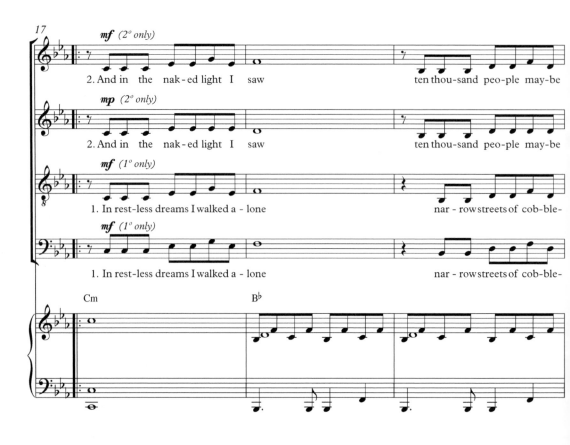

6

10

Moderate swing feeling ($\bullet$ = 136)

14

118 **Moderato, like a spiritual**

122

22

trou-bled wa-ter, I will lay me down.

trou-bled wa-ter, I will lay me down.

trou-bled wa-ter, I will lay me down.

trou-bled wa-ter, I will lay me down.

THIS MEDLEY OF THREE GREAT SIMON & GARFUNKEL SONGS INCLUDES THEIR
BREAKTHROUGH HIT THE SOUND OF SILENCE, SIMON'S LIGHT-HEARTED
CELEBRATION OF NEW YORK'S 59TH STREET BRIDGE (A.K.A FEELING GROOVY)
AND THEIR SOARING ANTHEM ABOUT A MORE METAPHORICAL BRIDGE
(BRIDGE OVER TROUBLED WATER).

ARRANGED FOR SATB CHOIR WITH PIANO ACCOMPANIMENT.

ALSO AVAILABLE FROM MUSIC SALES:

BEAUTIFUL (CHRISTINA AGUILERA)
SATB/PIANO – NOV170533
SSA/PIANO – NOV170544

BLACKBIRD (THE BEATLES)
SATB/PIANO – NO91300
SSA/PIANO – NO91289

FIELDS OF GOLD (STING)
SATB/PIANO – NOV940907
SSA/PIANO – NOV940918

HALLELUJAH (LEONARD COHEN, JEFF BUCKLEY AND OTHERS)
SATB/PIANO – NOV940863
SSA/PIANO – NOV940874

HERO (MARIAH CAREY, X FACTOR FINALISTS)
SATB/PIANO – NOV940830
SSA/PIANO – NOV940841

I HAVE A DREAM (ABBA)
SATB/PIANO – NOV170467
SSA/PIANO – NOV170478

KILLING ME SOFTLY WITH HIS SONG (ROBERTA FLACK, THE FUGEES)
SATB/PIANO – NOV170500
SSA/PIANO – NOV170522

MAN IN THE MIRROR (MICHAEL JACKSON)
SATB/PIANO – NOV941281
SSA/PIANO – NOV941094

REJOICE (KATHERINE JENKINS, IL DIVO)
SATB/PIANO – NOV940819

RULE THE WORLD (TAKE THAT)
SATB/PIANO – NOV940940
SSA/PIANO – NOV940951

RUN (SNOW PATROL, LEONA LEWIS)
SATB/PIANO – NOV940852

WONDERFUL TONIGHT (ERIC CLAPTON)
SATB/PIANO – NOV170489
SSA/PIANO – NOV170511

YOU RAISE ME UP (JOSH GROBAN, WESTLIFE AND OTHERS)
SATB/PIANO – NOV940929
SSA/PIANO – NOV940896

Novello Publishing Limited
part of The Music Sales Group
14-15 Berners Street
London W1T 3LJ, UK

Exclusive distributors:
Music Sales Limited
Newmarket Road
Bury St Edmunds
Suffolk IP33 3YB, UK

www.musicsales.com

This publication © 2013
Novello & Company Limited

Edited by Ruth Power

ISBN 978-1-78038-971-4

9 781780 389714